Getting Help with Gas

Keri-Michèle Lodge, Nigel Hollins and Sheila Hollins
illustrated by Lucy Bergonzi

Beyond Words

Leatherhead

3

7

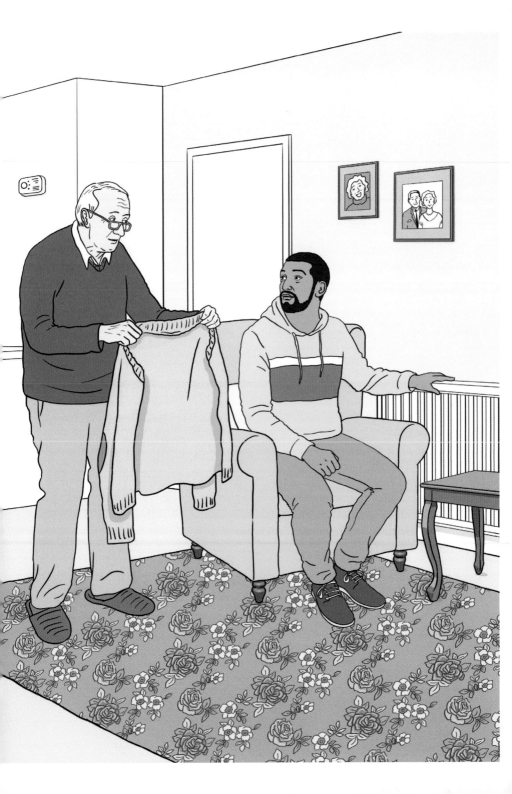

18

24

40

First published in the UK 2024 by Books Beyond Words.

Text & illustrations © Books Beyond Words, 2024.

No part of this book may be reproduced in any form, or by any means, without the prior permission in writing from the publisher.

ISBN 978-1-78458-187-9

British Library Cataloguing-in-Publication Data

A catalogue record for this book is available from the British Library.

Printed by Royal British Legion Industries, Leatherhead.

Books Beyond Words is a Charitable Incorporated Organisation (no. 1183942).

Further information about the Books Beyond Words series can be obtained from Beyond Words' website: www.booksbeyondwords.co.uk.

More information and resources

To find out more about this topic, please scan the QR code, or visit this link:
https://booksbeyondwords. co.uk/s/BBW-Getting-Help- with-Gas-resources.pdf

Authors and Artist

Keri-Michèle Lodge is a Consultant in Learning Disability Psychiatry at Leeds and York Partnership NHS Foundation Trust. Before becoming a doctor, she worked as a community support assistant, supporting adults with a learning disability to live in their own homes. She is also a sibling carer.

Nigel Hollins is the Co-Founder of Beyond Words and the original inspiration for our books. He has lived on his own, with support, for many years and shared his experiences for the creation of this book. Nigel has previously co-authored and advised on many different Beyond Words titles, including *The Drama Group* and *Peter's New Home*.

Sheila Hollins is the Founder, Lead Editor and Executive Chair of Beyond Words, and a family carer. She is Emeritus Professor of Psychiatry of Disability at St George's, University of London, and is a Member of the House of Lords. She is a past President of the Royal College of Psychiatrists, the British Medical Association and the Royal College of Occupational Therapists.

Lucy Bergonzi has worked as a muralist, theatre designer, community artist and art tutor. For many years she worked in the voluntary and community sector, with wide experience of supporting people with learning disabilities. She is the illustrator of several titles for Books Beyond Words, including *Belonging, Choosing My First Job, Beating the Virus* and *Love in Lockdown*. Lucy's website is: **www.lucybergonzi.co.uk**.

45

Acknowledgements

We are grateful for the generous support and advice of everyone who has helped us bring this book to life. Special thanks to the organisations, groups and people who trialled this book: Proactive community members including Emma Jane, Michael, Leanne and Robert, facilitated by Helen Guest Co-Production Manager at Active Prospects, Gravesend Book Club including Andy, Tony, James, Jamie, Manbir, Kashmira, Peter, Adrian, Lucy and Ricky, Dartford Book Club, other members of Kent Book Clubs including Julie, Sue and Marc, KeyRing Bexleyheath, and Sarah Cookson.

Our illustrator Lucy is grateful to her models Chris, Des, Luke, Rosie and Steve for their help when she was creating the pictures for *Getting Help with Gas*.

We'd like to extend a huge thank you to the funder of this book, Cadent.

More stories to enjoy

Belonging
Kali is lonely but helps Stefan during an emergency. She makes friends and starts to feel like she belongs.

Cooking with Friends
Choosing, cooking and eating food can be fun as well as being healthy and safe.

Ginger is a Hero
Mary doesn't get on with her neighbour. But when Mrs Hill has a fall, Mary and Ginger the cat help to save her life.

Find these, and our other titles, here:
www.booksbeyondwords.co.uk

How to read this book

You can read this book on your own, with another person or in a group. It is not necessary to be able to read or to speak any words at all.

Start at the beginning and encourage the reader to turn the pages themselves. Everyone can tell the story they see in their own way – with words, signs, facial expressions or whatever works for them. Whether you are reading the book with one person or with a group, encourage them to tell the story in their own words. You will discover what each person thinks is happening, what they already know and how they feel. You may think something different is happening in the pictures yourself, but that doesn't matter. Their interpretation tells you about their life experience.

Some people will follow the story without any problems. If a picture is more difficult, it can help to prompt with open questions, gradually going deeper into the meaning, for example:

- I wonder who that is?

- I wonder what is happening?

- What is he or she doing now?

- I wonder how he or she is feeling?

- Have you felt like that? Has it happened to you/ your friend/ your family?

You don't have to read the whole story in one sitting. Allow people time to follow the pictures at their own pace. Stay longer with any pictures they are drawn to.

48